The New Mental Health Act

01	What is 'The Mental Health Act' all about?	1
02	Advance statements	5

People

03	Named person	17
04	Independent advocacy	25
05	The rights of carers	31
06	Mental health officer (MHO)	39

Organisations

07	The Mental Welfare Commission	47
08	The Mental Health Tribunal	55
09	Health Boards and local authorities	65

Special Powers

10	Consent to treatment	73
11	Compulsory treatment orders	83
12	Emergency and short-term powers	91
13	People involved in criminal proceedings	103
14	How do I appeal?	125

Other Information

15	Words used in this guide	135
16	Where else can I get help or advice?	137

01 What is the Mental Health Act all about?

This is the new law which says how you can be treated if you have a mental disorder. It also says what your rights are.

Mental disorder are the words used in the law to describe someone who has

- **A mental illness**
- **A learning disability**
- **A personality disorder**

The new law says:

- when you can be given treatment even if you do not want it

- when you can be taken into hospital even if you do not want to

- what your rights are

- how your rights are protected.

What does the new law say about my rights?

The people who give you care and treatment should listen to:

- your views about your care and treatment.

- what you said about your care and treatment in the past.

- what some other people think about your care and treatment.

  - your carers

  - named person (someone you can choose to look out for you if you have to have treatment. They help decide about your care and treatment)

  - guardian (someone appointed by the court to make decisions for you if you are unable to decide for yourself)

  - Welfare Attorney (someone you choose to decide about your care and treatment if you become ill and cannot decide for yourself)

The people who give you care and treatment should tell you about:

■ your care and treatment

■ any choices you can make

■ what they think will work best for you

■ any help which you or your carer can get.

They must make sure that:

■ They know as much as possible about you and your life

■ You are treated as well as possible

■ If you have to be held for treatment it is for the shortest time needed

■ You have care as long as you need it

02 Advance statements

- What is an advance statement?
- What should I put in it?
- What does the witness do?
- Who can help me write it?
- When will it be used?
- Who should know about it?
- How can I change it?

What is an advance statement?

If you are ill, it is important that the people who look after you know about:

■ the treatment that works for you

■ the treatment that does not work for you

■ the treatment you do not want

■ why some treatments are better for you than others.

An advance statement lets you put these things in writing. You should write this when you are well enough to say what you want.

What should I put in my advance statement?

Your statement should have:

■ your name and address

■ the treatments you want

■ the treatments you do not want

■ the name and address of your witness

■ the job of your witness

■ the date your statement was witnessed.

You should also include the name and address of:

■ your named person

■ your carer

■ your GP

■ your guardian and welfare attorney if you have one.

[See the example form on pages 13 and 14.]

Named person: someone you choose to look out for you if you have to have treatment. They help to make decisions about your care and treatment.

Guardian: someone appointed by the court to make decisions for you if you are unable to decide for yourself.

Welfare Attorney: someone you choose to decide about your care and treatment if you become ill and cannot decide for yourself.

What does the witness do?

A **witness** must check and sign your statement. The witness checks that you understand what is in your statement. If they think that you do, they will ask you to sign it. They will also sign it.

Who can be a witness?

A witness can be:

- a doctor

- a nurse

- a lawyer

- a social worker

- an occupational therapist

- a clinical psychologist

- a supervisor or manager of a care service.

Who can help me write my advance statement?

Another person can write your statement. They must write what **you say** you want and need. They should not write what **they** think. People who could help.

- your family

- doctor or nurse

- mental health officer (a specially trained social worker who helps people who have a mental disorder)

- independent advocate (someone who helps you say what **you think** about your treatment)

- support worker.

When another person has written your statement, the witness makes sure that you agree with it. If they think that you do, they ask you to sign your statement. They also sign it.

Who should know about my advance statement?

You should give a copy to all those who are caring for you. For example:

■ carer

■ family

■ named person

- doctor

- nurse

- guardian

- welfare attorney

- independent advocate

- mental health officer

- solicitor.

You need to keep a list of everyone who has a copy of your advance statement. If you make any changes you need to tell all the people who have a copy.

When will my advance statement be used?

If you become ill, you may be unable to decide about your treatment. People caring for you should read your advance statement and think about your wishes. It helps them to decide what is best for you.

Ayesha's advance statement says she does not want Medicine XXXXX because it makes her feel ill. When the doctor reads this he/she decides to give Ayesha another medication.

Colin's advance statement says he wants to be given Medicine XXX because he thinks it helps him. The doctor reads this but cannot give Colin this because he/she knows it would not be right for him at this time. The doctor explains why in writing and gives this to Colin and all those caring for him.

How can I change my advance statement?

■ **You can review your advance statement**

This means you read it and decide if it is still OK for you. It is a good idea to do this every ⏱6 months or every ⏱12 months. You should also check the list of everyone who has a copy.

■ **You can withdraw your advance statement**

If you do this, you should write the words:

"I withdraw the advance statement made by me (write your name) on (write the date your statement was witnessed)"

The witness checks that you no longer want your advance statement. They sign and date this. **[See the sample form on pages 15 and 16]**

■ **You can change your advance statement**

You need to write a new advance statement and withdraw the old one. If you do this, the witness checks and signs both of these.

Advance statement

**Made Under
The Mental Health (Care And Treatment) (Scotland) Act 2003**

Your Name: _____

Your Address: _____

_____

If I _____ (your name) am ill in the future and not able to say what I think about my treatment I would like these views to be known.

1. I would like to receive the following treatments:

_____

_____

_____

2. I would not like to receive the following treatments:

_____

_____

_____

3. Your Signature _____

4. Your Witness should complete this part

I certify that in my opinion _____
[name of the person making the advance statement] is able to give
his/her wishes as they have done so.

I hereby witness his/her signature.

Signature _____

Date: _____

Full name of witness: _____

_____

Address of witness: _____

_____

_____

Job of witness: _____

**You should keep a list of the names of everyone who has a copy
of this document.**

Withdrawal of advance statement

Your Name: _____

Your Address: _____

I _____ [*your name*]

wish to withdraw my advance statement. This was signed and dated
on _____ and it was witnessed by

[*name of your witness*]

_____

Your Signature: _____

Your Witness should complete this part

2. Witness Certificate

I certify that in my opinion _____

[*name of person withdrawing advance statement*] is able to set down his wishes as above. I hereby witness his/her signature.

Your witness signs here: _____

The date of signing: _____

Full name of witness: _____

_____

Address of witness: _____

_____

_____

Job of witness: _____

You should keep a list of the names of everyone who has a copy of this document.

03 Named person

- What is a named person?
- What do they do?
- Who can I choose to be my named person?
- How do I nominate my named person?
- How can I change my named person?
- Who can be a witness?

What is a named person?

If you need treatment under the new Mental Health Act you can choose someone to look out for you. This person is called a named person. Anyone aged 16 or over can choose a named person.

Your named person can make important decisions about your care if you are not able to decide yourself. Because of this you should choose someone who knows you well and who you can trust.

You can have an independent advocate and a named person. Your advocate cannot be your named person because they have different jobs to do.

Your independent advocate is someone who helps **you say what you think** about your treatment.

What does my named person do?

■ They must be told about your care.

■ Anyone who gives you care and treatment must ask your named person what they think.

■ Your named person can ask the Mental Health Tribunal to decide about your care. They can go to the Tribunal and give their views. The Tribunal decides about the compulsory treatment of people with mental disorder.

■ They agree (or not agree) to medical examinations of you where they are needed for a Compulsory Treatment Order. This means you have treatment even if you do not want it.

■ They can ask the Local Authority or Health Board to assess your needs.

Who can I choose to be my named person?

Anyone aged 16 or over can be your named person. The person must understand what is involved.

Your named person can be:

- Your carer

- Your partner

- Your nearest relative (mum, dad, brother or sister, or cousin)

- Another service user

- Anyone else you choose

Your named person should not be anyone with responsibility for your care like your GP or mental health officer.

Mental health officer: a specially trained social worker who helps people who have a mental disorder. He/she should tell you about your rights and make sure you get the care you need.

How can I nominate my named person?

Once someone agrees to be your named person you need to write down that you chose them to be your named person. This is called a "nomination".

A nomination must be:

■ Signed by you

■ Signed and dated by a witness

The witness must say that you understand about choosing a named person and that you have not been put under pressure by anyone.

What if I do not choose a named person?

If you are 16 or over and decide not to choose a named person your main adult carer becomes your named person. If you don't have an adult carer or they don't want to be your named person it will be your nearest relative.

How can I change my named person?

Gina is not happy with her named person, her cousin Rita. She makes a written statement saying she no longer wants Rita to be her named person. Gina signs the statement and asks her nurse to witness the statement. She then chooses a new named person.

Can I stop someone from being a named person?

Sean does not want his brother to be his named person. He makes a written statement saying he does not want this. He asks his social worker to be his witness. They both sign and date the statement.

Can anyone else change my named person?

Yes. If some people think your named person is not suitable they can ask the Tribunal to change this. The people who can do this include your mental health officer, your Responsible Medical Officer (this will usually be the consultant who is in charge of your care) and your relatives.

If you are not happy with a named person the Tribunal chooses for you, you can apply to the Tribunal to change this person.

Who can be a witness?

A witness can be:

■ a doctor

■ a nurse

■ a lawyer

■ a social worker

■ an occupational therapist

■ a clinical psychologist

■ a supervisor or manager of a care service

04 Independent advocacy

- What does the law say?
- What is independent advocacy?
- Why might I need it?
- When might I need it?
- Who will help me get it?
- Where can I get more information?

What does the law say?

Under the new Act people with learning disabilities and people with a mental illness have a right to independent advocacy. You do not have to be in hospital to get this right.

This means that you should be able to have an independent advocate and/or join an advocacy group if you want to.

What is independent advocacy?

Independent advocacy helps you to make your voice stronger and to have as much control as possible over your life.

It is called **independent** because advocates and advocacy workers are *separate from services*. They do not work for hospitals, social work or other services.

There are different types of advocacy:

- **self advocacy:** people come together in groups to speak up about things that are important to them. Self-advocacy groups try to change the way people feel about themselves and change other people's attitudes. They also try to change services and policies. This is also called **collective advocacy**.

- **professional advocacy:** an independent advocate works with you to help you sort out your problem. The advocate might be paid or be a volunteer.

- **citizen advocacy:** an ordinary member of the public gets to know you well over a long period of time. They stand alongside you and help you to get what you need.

Why might I need independent advocacy?

Some people need support to speak up, to understand what is being said and to make decisions. Many people find that when they feel ill or upset they are not as good at saying what they want and they need support to speak up.

Moira has a learning disability. She wants some help for an important meeting with the housing department. Her advocate, Joe, helps her decide what she wants to say and goes to the meeting with her to help her to say it.

When might I need independent advocacy?

There are some times when it is especially important for you to get advocacy support.

1. In hospital

2. On an order which says that:

■ you must stay in hospital

■ you can only stay out of hospital on certain conditions

■ you can be given treatment even if you do not want it.

Your doctors, nurses, social workers and mental health officers should make sure you know about independent advocacy and help you get it. They should make sure it is free.

They should give you accessible information (for example in large print).

3. Going to a Tribunal meeting

Selma's illness has got worse. Her mental health officer wants her to have treatment. Selma does not agree and her mental health officer asks the Tribunal to decide. He helps Selma find an independent advocate to help her give her views. The advocate helps Selma to say what _she thinks_ at the tribunal meeting.

Mental health officer: a specially trained social worker who helps people who have a mental disorder. He/she should tell you about your rights and make sure you get the care you need.

Mental Health Tribunal: the organisation that decides about the compulsory treatment of people with mental disorder.

Where can I get more information?

You can find out more from:

■ People First (Scotland)

■ Scottish Independent Advocacy Alliance

■ Your local social work and health services will tell you how to contact advocacy services near you.

05 The rights of carers

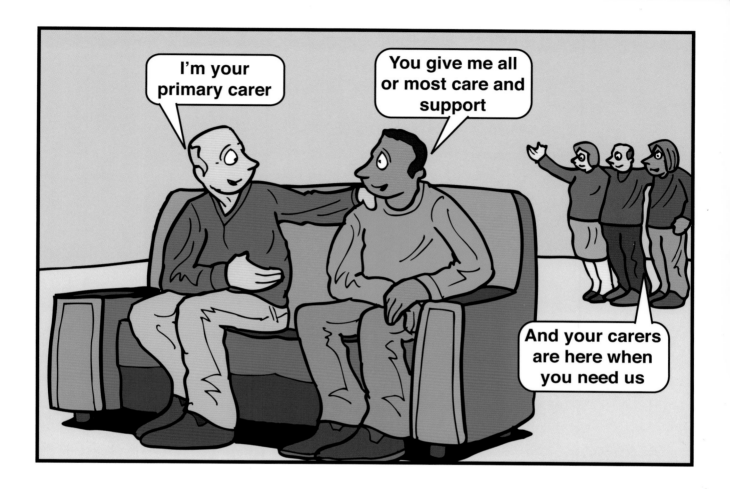

■ Who is a carer?

■ Who is my primary carer?

■ What are my carer's rights?

■ How is my carer different from others who help me?

■ Who can my carer ask for support?

Who is a carer?

The new law says a carer is someone who gives you care and support when you need it. Your carer could be:

- your husband/wife

- your partner

- a friend

- a relative

- a neighbour.

You can have more than one carer.

They can care for you and support you in different ways. For example, they can help with shopping, cooking and cleaning. They can listen to your problems and help you make decisions.

One of Stevie's carers is his friend, Duncan. Duncan helps Stevie with his shopping and cooking. He also takes him swimming every week and goes with him to the doctor's surgery.

A 'carer' is someone who helps you because **they want to help you**. It is not their job to do this. If someone helps you as part of their job they are not called carers. For example a home help is not called a 'carer' because it is their job.

Who is my primary carer?

Your primary carer is the person who gives you **all or most of** your care and support. If you have more than one carer they must decide who the primary carer is. You can help to decide this. You can only have one primary carer.

Stevie talks to the people who care for him and to Duncan. They all decide that Duncan should be his primary carer because he gives him most help.

What are my carer's rights?

When doctors and others decide about your care and treatment they should:

- find out what your carer thinks

- think about your carer's rights

- give your carer any information they need. They only do this if you agree. You can say if you do not want your carer to know some things. (If doctors or others believe you may not be safe because of your illness they tell your carer even if you disagree.)

Stevie's carer, Duncan, thinks Stevie's illness is getting worse. He asks the local authority and the Health Board to assess Stevie's needs. This means they should find out what care and treatment he needs.

■ your carer is told by police if you need to be taken to a place of safety. The police do this if you are ill and need care and treatment immediately

■ if you are in hospital, your primary carer is told if you have to be changed to another hospital in Scotland

■ your carer can go to the Tribunal and tell them about your care and treatment needs.

Mental Health Tribunal: the organisation that decides about the compulsory treatment of people with mental disorder.

How is my carer different from others who help me?

If you are ill and need care and treatment there are other people who help you.

Named person

■ this is someone you choose to look after your interests if you need treatment. They help to decide about your care and treatment

■ a carer is not the same as the named person. A named person has other rights under the law

■ you can choose your carer to be your named person. If you do not choose a named person then the new law makes your primary carer your named person.

Independent advocate?

■ an independent advocate is called "independent" because they are not tied to other services. Your doctor, hospital or social work department can help you find an independent advocate

■ an independent advocate helps you **say what you think** about your care and treatment. They do not say what they think

■ your carer can say **what they think** about your care and treatment.

Who can my carer ask for support?

If your carer has questions about your care and treatment or their own needs or rights they can contact the Mental Welfare Commission. The Mental Welfare Commission that looks after those who need help because of a mental disorder. They make sure all treatment follows the law.

They have a free phone advice line.

Service user and carer free phone: 0800 389 6809 ☏

Mental Welfare Commission for Scotland ✉

Floor K, Argyle House

3 Lady Lawson Street

EDINBURGH EH3 9SH

Telephone: 0131 222 6111

Website: www.mwcscot.org.uk

06 Mental health officer

- What is a mental health officer?
- When might I have a mental health officer?
- What does my mental health officer do?
  - Emergency and short-term powers
  - Compulsory treatment orders
  - People involved with police and courts
- Can I change my mental health officer?

What is a mental health officer?

A mental health officer is a social worker who has special training and experience in working with people who have a mental disorder.

When might I have a mental health officer?

If you become ill and do not agree to treatment, you can be put under compulsory measures. For example you can be:

■ held for a short time for doctors to examine you

■ given treatment even if you do not want it

■ taken into hospital for treatment even if you do not want to.

If this happens your social work department must appoint a mental health officer to help you.

What does my mental health officer do?

Your mental health officer:

■ finds out what you need

■ tells you about your rights

■ writes reports and care plans

■ agrees that you need to be examined by a doctor

■ asks for you to have a compulsory treatment order if you need this. This means you have treatment even if you do not want it.

Emergency and short-term powers

■ If you are living in the community and become ill your mental health officer must find out if you need care and treatment.

John is living at home but he is ill. Ali, his mental health officer, must find out what John needs. Ali asks the court for permission to come into John's home. He also asks the court for permission for a doctor to examine John.

■ Emergency detention certificate

This means you can be kept in hospital and have treatment for no more than ⏱3 days.

John's doctor decides that he needs an emergency detention certificate. The doctor asks Ali, his mental health officer, if he agrees. Ali talks to John and the doctor and then tells the doctor he agrees.

■ A short-term detention certificate

This means you can be kept in hospital and given treatment for up to ⏱28 days.

The doctor wants to put John on a short-term detention certificate. The doctor asks Ali, his mental health officer, if he agrees. Ali talks to John and tells him about his rights to a named person, an independent advocate or a solicitor. He helps John to find these people to help him. Ali talks to the doctor and tells him he agrees.

Compulsory treatment orders

Your mental health officer may decide that you need a compulsory treatment order.

Your mental health officer asks the Mental Health Tribunal to decide if you need compulsory treatment. The Tribunal is the organisation that decides about the compulsory treatment of people with mental disorder.

If your mental health officer asks for a compulsory treatment order they should:

■ tell you and your named person

■ tell you about your rights

■ help you find an independent advocate

■ help you find a solicitor

■ help you find extra communication support if you need it.

If you are involved with the police or courts

If you are involved with the police and the courts, they must:

■ make sure you have a mental health officer to help you

■ ask your mental health officer for advice

■ ask your mental health officer to prepare a Social Circumstances Report. This is a special report which has all the information about your situation – past and present. The mental health officer must prepare this within ☺21 days if you are put under an order by the court.

The mental health officer gives this report to the court to help them decide what to do about your care and treatment. They give a copy to you, your doctor and the Mental Welfare Commission.

If your mental health officer decides this report would not be useful he/she must tell the Mental Welfare Commission and your doctor.

Your mental health officer gives advice and reports if you are put under any of these orders by the court:

- Assessment Order

- Treatment Order

- Interim Compulsion Order

- Compulsion Order

- Restriction Order

- Hospital Direction

- Transfer for treatment

You can read more about these orders on page 87.

Can I change my Mental Health Officer?

Yes. If you cannot work with your mental health officer your social work department helps to sort out the problem or chooses a new mental health officer for you.

You may want to change your mental health officer because you do not agree with his/her decisions. A new mental health officer may make the same decisions about your care and treatment.

07 The Mental Welfare Commission

- What does the Mental Welfare Commission (Commission) do?

- Who can contact the Commission?

- How do I speak to the Commission?

- What if I need more help?

- How does the Commission make sure everyone follows the law?

- What if I am not happy with the Commission?

What does the Mental Welfare Commission (Commission) do?

If you have a mental disorder, the Commission should make sure:

- your care and treatment follows the new law

- your rights are looked after

- your rights are looked after even when you cannot make decisions for yourself.

They also help if you are cared for by the Adults with Incapacity law especially if you have a welfare guardian.

The people who work for the Commission are called Commissioners. They are chosen because they know about mental disorder.

They may:

- work in mental health like doctors, nurses, social workers, care workers

- have used mental health services themselves

- have cared for someone with a mental disorder.

Adults with Incapacity Law – this law looks after people who cannot decide things for themselves.

Welfare guardian. This is someone the court chooses to decide about your care and welfare if you cannot do this.

Who can contact the Commission?

You – if you are worried about your care and treatment.

Your carer – if they are worried about your care and treatment or if they need more support.

People who work in care services – if they want advice and information on the law.

Your Independent advocate – if they want advice about your care.

Your named person – if they are unhappy with your care.

Independent advocate is someone who helps you to say what you think about your care and treatment.

Named person is someone you choose to look out for you if you have to have treatment. They help to decide about your care and treatment.

How do I speak to the Commission?

If you or your carer want to ask about your rights you can call 0800 389 6809 ☎ (open 9 - 5 from Monday - Friday). This is a free phone advice line.

The person you speak to:

■ helps you understand what the law says about care and treatment

■ tells you what you can do if you are not happy with your care and treatment

■ tells you about other groups who may be able to help you.

There are also information leaflets which you can ask for by phone or you can get them from the website www.mwcscot.org.uk

Marek has been put on a compulsory treatment order. This means he must have treatment even though he does not want it. His carer phones to ask what the law says about this. The person who answers explains the law. He explains that Marek must have the treatment. He also tells Marek's carer how to get him support from an independent advocate.

What if I need more help?

If you need more help the Commission may:

■ ask you more about your problem

■ talk to the people who are treating you

■ tell those who are treating you what is wrong

■ ask them to put it right

■ check with you and your carer to see if things have got better.

The Commission may visit you in hospital, in a care home, at a care service or in your own home.

They might visit if you:

■ have asked for a visit

■ are on a compulsory treatment order

■ have a welfare guardian.

Compulsory treatment order means you have treatment even if you do not want it.

Some weeks later Marek is still on a compulsory treatment order and in hospital. The Commission come to visit Marek and his carer. They ask him about his treatment. They want to find out if there are any problems or if he needs any more support.

How does the Commission make sure everyone follows the law?

Anyone who gives you care and treatment should tell the Commission if:

■ you have been held under the law

■ you must have compulsory treatment

■ the doctor has not followed your wishes in your advance statement. This is when you write down how you would like to be treated if you become ill in the future

■ a welfare guardian is appointed.

If there is a problem, the Commission:

■ looks at all the information and decide what is best for you

■ suggests changes to make sure it doesn't happen again.

The Commission shares information in reports. This helps those giving care and treatment to learn more about the best way to care for you and others.

What if I am not happy with the Commission?

If you are not happy about how the Commission has helped you can complain.

1. You can phone **0800 389 6809** ☎. The Commission should tell you how to complain. They should do this in writing. They should find out what has happened from you and others. They should tell you what they have found out and tell you what happens next.

2. If you are still unhappy you can complain to the Scottish Public Services Ombudsman. The telephone number is 0870 011 5378 ☎. The Scottish Public Services Ombudsman listens to complaints about public services.

08 The Mental Health Tribunal

- **What is the Mental Health Tribunal?**
- **What does the Tribunal do?**
- **How do I contact the Tribunal?**
- **What happens if I have a Tribunal hearing?**
  - **before the hearing?**
  - **at the hearing?**
  - **after the hearing?**
- **What if I disagree with the Tribunal?**

What is the Mental Health Tribunal?

The Tribunal is an independent organisation set up by the new law. It decides what to do if you need compulsory treatment order. This means you have treatment even if you do not want it.

The Tribunal has a President and 300 members around Scotland.

There are 3 kinds of members:

- lawyers

- doctors

- others like nurses or social workers who know about mental disorder.

If you have a Tribunal meeting there will be a group of 3 people – 1 from each of these groups. This group is called the tribunal **panel**. The person who chairs the tribunal is called the **convenor**.

A Tribunal meeting is often called a **'hearing'**. The Tribunal must hear and read all the information about you and your case. They then decide what to do about your care and treatment.

Compulsory treatment order means you have treatment even if you do not want it.

What does the Tribunal do?

The Tribunal decides about your treatment if you need to have compulsory treatment. For example:

If you **need** a compulsory treatment order

■ If your mental health officer thinks that you need a compulsory treatment order he/she must ask the Tribunal to decide.

If you **have** a compulsory treatment order

■ Your doctor can ask the Tribunal to change your care and treatment.

■ You, your named person or the Mental Welfare Commission can ask the Tribunal to review your case. Review means they think about all the information again and decide if you still need the order. The Tribunal must review your case once every ⏲2 years.

Colm has a compulsory treatment order. He thinks he is now much better. He wants to ask the Tribunal to review his case. His named person, Sheila, helps him to do this.

Named person: someone you choose to look out for you if you have to have treatment. They help to make decisions about your care and treatment.

Mental Welfare Commission: the organisation that looks after those who need help because of a mental disorder. They make sure all treatment follows the law. You can speak to them at any time if you are unhappy about your care and treatment.

If you have a short-term detention certificate

A short-term detention certificate means you can be held in hospital to get care and treatment. This lasts for ⏱28 days.

■ You can appeal to the Tribunal against this.

If you are being held more securely than you think is needed

■ You can ask the Tribunal to review your case.

If you are involved with the police or courts and having treatment in hospital

■ Your doctor might ask the Tribunal for changes to your care and treatment.

■ You and/or your named person can ask the Tribunal to review your case.

Appeal means you ask the court or the Tribunal to change their decision.

How do I contact the Tribunal?

You can write or phone the Tribunal office. You can ask your named person, independent advocate or solicitor to help you to do this.

Colm writes to the Tribunal office. He tells them his name, his doctor's name and his hospital. Sheila helps him with the letter.

Service user and carer freephone: 0800 345 70 60 📞
Mental Health Tribunal for Scotland ✉
1st Floor Bothwell House
Hamilton Business Park, Caird Park
HAMILTON ML3 0QA
telephone: 01698 390 000
website: www.mhtscot.gov.uk

What happens before the hearing?

Before the hearing, workers at the Tribunal office send Colm all the information he needs.

- The time

- The place

- How to get there

- How to claim travel and other expenses

- Who will be there on the day

- What will happen at the hearing

Who goes to the Tribunal hearing?

- You

- Those who care for you and support you. This may be your:

  - named person

  - guardian

  - welfare attorney

  - carer

  - independent advocate

  - solicitor

- The 3 Tribunal members

- Those responsible for your care and treatment:

  - nurse

  - mental health officer

  - doctor (GP)

  - doctor (RMO)

If you ask a solicitor to help you at the hearing you should be able to get legal aid. Legal aid is money to help you pay a solicitor. Your solicitor can help you to do this.

Independent advocate. Someone who helps you say what you think about your treatment. They are called "independent" because they are not tied to other services.

What happens at the hearing?

When Colm and Sheila arrive at the hearing, the clerk shows them where everything is. The convenor explains the rules about the hearing and what will happen.

The panel reads all the information about the case. This includes reports from Colm's doctor and his mental health officer. They listen to Colm and everyone else.

They try to decide what to do on the day of the hearing. If they cannot decide, the hearing carries on at a later date.

Sometimes they make an order for you to get the care and treatment you need until a final decision is made.

What happens after the hearing?

The Tribunal may tell you their decision at the end of the hearing or they may write to you after the hearing.

The Tribunal tells everyone who needs to know about their decision. This may be:

■ your doctor

■ your mental health officer

■ the Mental Welfare Commission

■ the court (if your case has come to the Tribunal from the court).

The Tribunal writes to Colm after the hearing. They tell him that he must stay on his compulsory treatment order. They give him information about how to appeal.

What If I disagree with the decision?

You may be able to appeal to the court. Appeal means you ask them to think again about the Tribunal's decision. The Tribunal should give you information about how to make an appeal.

Do you always have a hearing?

If you and those responsible for your care and treatment agree the Tribunal can decide without a hearing. If you **do not agree** the Tribunal must have a hearing.

09 Health Boards and local authorities

■ How should my local authority help me?

■ How do they help to keep me safe?

■ What happens if I am too ill to make decisions?

■ What happens if I refuse to have treatment?

■ How should my Health Board help me?

■ How do they work together?

How should my local authority help me?

Your local authority should give you care and support services when you are not in hospital. This is to help you to live as well as possible.

They should help you to:

- find a suitable home

- have training

- find a job or to keep a job you already have

- take part in leisure activities

- to travel to do these things.

If you are in hospital they may still be able to help.

How should my local authority help to keep me safe?

Your local authority should make enquiries if it thinks that you are not safe. This means they should find out what you need to keep you safe.

They do this if they think:

- there is a problem with your care or treatment

- your property may be lost or damaged

- you are unable to look after your money

- some other person may be unsafe because of your illness.

Local authorities must employ mental health officers. Mental health officers have special training to help people who have a mental disorder. They:

- prepare care plans

- prepare reports

- tell you about your rights.

Your local authority can ask others to help:

- Mental Welfare Commission

- Public Guardian

- Care Commission

- Health Board

Mental health officer: a specially trained social worker who helps people who have a mental disorder. He/she should tell you about your rights and make sure you get the care you need.

What happens if I am ill and cannot decide about treatment ?

Your mental health officer:

- talks to you if you need to be detained under the Act. Detained means you are taken to hospital for treatment. You have to stay in hospital even if you do not want this

- applies for a compulsory treatment order (CTO).

This means you have treatment even if you do not want this.

If you need these things, your mental health officer must tell your named person and the Mental Welfare Commission.

What happens if I refuse to have treatment?

Chrissie is ill but refuses to speak to her mental health officer, Elaine. Elaine asks the court for special permission to come to Chrissie's home and to see her medical records. The court also gives Elaine permission to hold Chrissie for up to 3 hours until a doctor examines her.

Named person: someone you choose to look out for you if you have to have treatment.

Mental Welfare Commission: the organisation that looks after those who need help because of a mental disorder. They make sure all treatment follows the law. You can speak to them at any time if you are unhappy about your care and treatment.

How should my Health Board help me?

Your Health Board should give you care and treatment if you are ill.

They should have doctors with special training to help people with a mental disorder. They should keep a list of these doctors in their area.

Mother and baby

They should help you to care for your child in hospital if you want to. Your child should be under 1 year old.

Shannon has a new baby. She feels a bit depressed. Her doctor says she should go to hospital for treatment. Shannon is worried about her baby. The doctor tells her the hospital will help her to look after the baby in hospital.

How do they work together?

Your Health Board and your local authority must work together to help you.

The Health Board must help the local authority when they are making enquiries about you.

Local authorities and NHS Boards must make sure that you can have an independent advocate.

An independent advocate gives you support and helps you to tell others what you think about your care and treatment. They are called "independent" because they are not tied to other services. Your doctor, hospital or social work department should help you find an independent advocate.

What if I am under 18?

If you need to go to hospital your **Health Board** should give you the services and living space you need.

They should do this whether you agreed to go to hospital or have been told to go to hospital.

Your local authority should make sure you get your education.

They must support you and your parent or guardian. They must help you both if the treatment is causing difficulties for your relationship.

10 Consent to treatment

- What happens when I need treatment?
- How does my doctor decide?
- What kinds of treatment can I have?
- How can I give my views?
- What should my doctor do?
- What are the special rules about treatment?
- Can I be forced to have treatment?

What happens when I need treatment?

If you consent

If you **consent** to have treatment, this means **you agree**. You are a "voluntary patient". You cannot be given treatment you do not want.

If you do not consent

You may not want the treatment or you may be too ill to decide. The new law says when you can be given treatment even if you do not want it. This is called compulsory treatment.

If you are unable to consent

You may be treated under a new law which helps you when you are unable to decide things for yourself. This is the Adults with Incapacity Act.

How does my doctor decide I need compulsory treatment?

Sam has a mental disorder. His doctor, Dr Rezal thinks that if she has treatment it will help her. She also thinks Sam will not be safe if she does not have treatment. Sam is too ill to decide so Dr Rezal decides to use the special powers in the new law.

You can be given compulsory treatment if you are under one of these orders:

■ **An emergency detention certificate**

■ You can be kept in hospital and given treatment for no more than 3 days.

■ **A short-term detention certificate**

■ You can be kept in hospital and given treatment for up to 28 days.

■ **A compulsory treatment order**

■ You can be given treatment if the Tribunal has agreed.

What kind of treatment can I be given?

How can I give my views?

Your doctor should think about your needs and:

- listen to you, your carer, your named person, independent advocate, or guardian

- read your advance statement when you write down how you would like to be treated if you become ill in the future

- give you information about the treatment

- help you to decide.

Independent advocate: someone who helps you say what you think about your treatment. They are called 'independent' because they are not tied to other services. Your doctor, hospital or social work department should help you find an independent advocate.

Named person: someone you choose to look out for you if you have to have treatment. They help to make decisions about your care and treatment.

What should my doctor do?

■ Your doctor should decide if you are able to agree to your treatment and you should agree in writing.

■ If your doctor thinks you are not able to agree he/she should explain in writing:

   ■ why you are not able to decide

   ■ how the treatment should help you.

■ He/she can then give you the treatment and explain the reasons in writing.

Dr Rezal talks to Sam and his independent advocate Harry. Harry helps Sam to explain what he thinks to the doctor. Dr Rezal decides that Sam is not able to agree to the treatment. She explains in writing why she thinks this. She also explains how the treatment will help Sam.

What are the special rules about treatment?

The law has special rules about some treatments. For example:

■ When your doctor wants to continue your medicine after ⏱2 months.

■ When you are not eating because of a mental disorder, you may be fed by a tube into the stomach.

■ When your doctor wishes you to have Electro-Convulsive Therapy (ECT) You cannot be given ECT if you are able to decide and you do not want it.

For these treatments your doctor should make sure that:

■ the treatment is the best thing for you

■ you are able to agree

■ you agree in writing.

If you are not able to agree or do not want to agree, a second doctor must examine you and agree. This doctor will be appointed by the Mental Welfare Commission.

Mental Welfare Commission: the organisation that looks after those who need help because of a mental disorder. They make sure all treatment follows the law. You can speak to them at any time if you are unhappy about your care and treatment.

Neurosurgery

Neurosurgery is an operation on the brain. If your doctor wants to do this:

1. He/she must make sure that it is the best thing for you. He/she must also make sure that you are able to agree in writing.

2. A second doctor must also say it is the best thing for you and that you are able to agree in writing.

AND

Two people (not doctors), chosen by the Mental Welfare Commission, must say that you are able to agree in writing.

If your doctor thinks that you are not able to agree, you can only be given the treatment if:

■ You do not resist the treatment.

■ A second doctor and two other people (not doctors) chosen by the Mental Welfare Commission, agree that it is the best thing for you.

■ The court agrees.

Urgent treatment

If you are held in hospital, you can be given treatment to:

■ save your life

■ stop your illness getting worse

■ stop your suffering

■ stop you from being violent

■ stop you from hurting yourself or someone else.

The doctor must tell the Mental Welfare Commission and explain why you needed the treatment.

Can I be forced to have treatment?

If you are in hospital for compulsory treatment:

■ force can only be used if necessary.

If you are in your own home:

■ force cannot be used to give you treatment.

If you are on a compulsory treatment in the community:

■ you can be taken to hospital and force can be used.

If you are unhappy about the use of force in your treatment, you can complain. Your named person or independent advocate can help you.

What if I do not agree with my treatment?

■ You should talk to your doctor. Your named person or your independent advocate can help you. Your doctor should tell why he/she thinks the treatment is the best thing for you.

■ If you still do not agree you can ask the Mental Health Tribunal to decide.

■ If you want to do this you can ask a solicitor for advice. You can get legal aid to pay for the solicitor's help.

Mental Health Tribunal: the organisation that decides about the compulsory treatment of people with mental disorder.

11 Compulsory treatment orders

■ What is a compulsory treatment order?

■ When might I get a compulsory treatment order?

■ Who decides if need a compulsory treatment order?

■ What are my rights?

■ How can I change my compulsory treatment order?

■ When does a compulsory treatment order end?

What is a compulsory treatment order?

A compulsory treatment order says some things that you have to do.

Some of these things might be that:

- you have to stay in hospital

- you have to go for medical treatment

- you have to go to certain services

- you have to stay at a particular pace in the community.

A compulsory treatment order lasts for ○6 months and can be renewed for another ○6 months. After that it can be renewed for periods of ○12 months.

When might I get a compulsory treatment order?

A compulsory treatment order can be made:

■ if medical treatment is available to help you

■ and If you don't get that treatment there is a big risk to you or someone else

■ and you are not able to make decisions about your treatment.

John's mental health officer, Kathleen, decides that John will not be safe if he does not have treatment. John is not able to decide about this. Kathleen decides she should ask the Tribunal for a compulsory treatment order. This means John will have treatment even though he does not want it.

Who decides if I need a compulsory treatment order?

Your mental health officer applies to the Tribunal. The Tribunal is the organisation that decides whether a compulsory treatment order should be made.

The application must include:

- 2 medical reports by doctors who examined you

- a report by the mental health officer

- a care plan saying the care and treatment you get if you are put on the order.

Mental health officer: a specially trained social worker who helps people who have a mental disorder. He/she should tell you about your rights and make sure you get the care you need.

John's mental health officer, Kathleen, sends the reports and care plans to the Tribunal. She tells John and his named person, Joe, that she is asking for a compulsory treatment order. She also explains John's rights to him.

You and your named person must be told if an application for a compulsory treatment order is made. Your mental health officer must explain your rights to you.

- You have the right to make your views heard by the Tribunal.

- You have the right to appeal against a compulsory treatment order. Appeal means you ask the Tribunal to change their decision.

- You have the right to an independent advocate. This is someone who helps you say what you think about your treatment. Your mental health officer must give you information about advocacy services and help you to contact them if you want to.

■ You can get legal advice from a solicitor. You should get legal aid to cover the costs of this. The solicitor might be able to help you get an independent medical report if you want to challenge the application for a compulsory treatment order.

The Tribunal must listen to your views and the views of your named person. The Tribunal must also take your advance statement into account. Advance statement is when you write down how you would like to be treated if you become ill in the future.

John goes to the Tribunal with his named person, Joe. They give the Tribunal their views. The Tribunal also read John's advance statement. They read all the other information about John and discuss what is best. They decide John should have a compulsory treatment order.

Temporary compulsory treatment order

The Tribunal can make a temporary compulsory treatment order while they get more information about your needs. A temporary compulsory treatment order can last for up to ⏱28 days. The total time you can be on temporary compulsory treatment orders cannot be for more than ⏱56 days.

How can I change my compulsory treatment order?

The doctor in charge of your care can apply to the Tribunal to change your order. You or your named person can do this too.

John's compulsory treatment order says he must go the hospital every week to have treatment. John would like to have this treatment at his GP surgery. John decides to ask the Tribunal to change the compulsory treatment order.

Treatment

There are special rules about some treatments like ECT. If you are on a compulsory treatment order you can also be given treatment in an emergency.

When does a compulsory treatment order end?

Your Responsible Medical Officer (consultant), or the Tribunal can end your compulsory treatment order if they don't think you need it anymore. The Mental Welfare Commission can ask your doctor or the Tribunal to end your compulsory treatment order.

12 Emergency and short-term powers

What does the law say about emergency powers?

Who can help in an emergency?

Who has emergency powers?

- ■ **Police**
- ■ **Local authority**
- ■ **Nurse**

What is an emergency detention certificate?

What is a short-term detention certificate?

How do I appeal?

What does the law say?

Sometimes when you become ill you need care and treatment very quickly. Emergency and short-term powers make sure you get the help you need. The new law says when:

- police can take you to a safe place for care and treatment

- your local authority can find out if you need care and treatment

- your nurse can keep you in hospital

- you can be given a emergency detention certificate. This means you can be kept in hospital for ⏱3 days and given treatment if you need it very quickly

- you can be given a short-term detention certificate. This means you can be kept in hospital and have treatment for ⏱28 days.

You should remember that the police may use these special powers to help you when you are ill. **This does not mean that you have done anything wrong.** They are using the powers to help you.

There are other powers in the new law which are used if someone is involved with the police or courts because they have done something wrong.

Who can help in an emergency?

If you or someone you know is ill and needs care and treatment urgently you may ask:

- a doctor
- a community psychiatric nurse
- a community learning disability nurse
- a social worker.

You might have other support in your area. Your social work service should tell you who can help.

If you think someone is in danger or a danger to others you should **phone 999**.

How do the police use these emergency powers?

If you are in a public place and a police officer thinks:

- you have a mental disorder
- you need care and treatment immediately.

The police officer can take you to a safe place. A safe place could be a hospital or a care home. Sometimes it may be the police station.

Remember that the police will take you to a safe place to help you. It does not mean you have done anything wrong.

The police must tell all of these people:

- your local authority (**Social Work Department**)

- your family or carer

- the Mental Welfare Commission. This is the organisation who looks after those who need help because of a mental disorder. They make sure all treatment follows the law.

The police get a doctor to examine you. The doctor may decide:

- you don't need any medical treatment

- you need treatment and they discuss this with you

- you need an emergency detention certificate

- you need a short-term detention certificate.

Morag is in the shopping centre. Some people are worried that she is ill and needs help. They call the police who take Morag to the local hospital. They get a doctor to examine her. The doctor decides she needs to stay in hospital for treatment. Morag agrees to have treatment.

How would the local authority use these powers?

Your local authority must find out what you need if you have a mental disorder. If they think:

- you are unable to look after yourself
- you are not safe
- your property is not safe
- someone else is not safe.

Your mental health officer can ask the court for help to find out about your needs. He/she can ask the court for permission.

- to come into your home
- to ask a doctor to examine you
- to take you to a "place of safety".

The doctor should take time to discuss your treatment with you. You have the right to ask questions about your treatment.

Your doctor may decide:

- you don't need any medical treatment
- you need treatment and you agree this together
- you need an emergency detention certificate
- you need a short-term detention certificate.

Mental health officer: a specially trained social worker who helps people who have a mental disorder. He/she should tell you about your rights and make sure you get the care you need.

How would a nurse use these powers?

If you are in hospital for treatment and you decide to leave the nurse may not agree. He/she can keep you in hospital for up to ⏱2 hours so that a doctor can see you.

If your nurse believes:

■ you may not be safe

■ someone else may not be safe

■ you need to be examined by a doctor.

Morag is in hospital having voluntary treatment. She wants to leave hospital but the nurse thinks she might not be safe if she left. The nurse uses the special powers to keep Morag in hospital for ⏱2 hours. She asks the doctor to examine Morag.

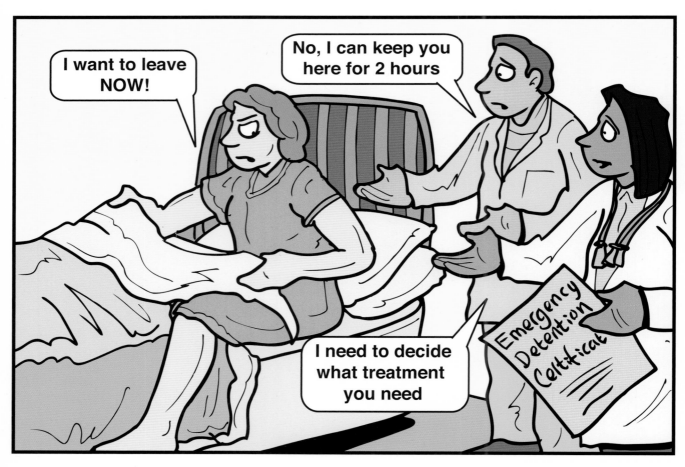

If the nurse uses this power he/she must:

- record it in writing

- tell the hospital managers

- tell the Mental Welfare Commission.

The doctor may decide:

- you don't need any medical treatment

- you need treatment. They will discuss it with you

- you need an emergency detention certificate

- you need a short-term detention certificate.

The doctor examines Morag and decides she needs more time to decide what is best. She gives her an emergency detention certificate. In the next ⏱3 days she talks to Morag and her carer about her care and treatment.

What is an emergency detention certificate?

The doctor uses this if he/she believes:

■ you have a mental disorder

■ you are not able to decide about your treatment

■ you need to stay in hospital

■ you or someone else may not be safe if you are not in hospital.

The doctor must ask your mental health officer to agree

↓

You should be taken to hospital within 3 days. This should be done with care for you.

↓

You can be kept in hospital for another 3 days. You should not be given treatment unless you agree.

↓

The hospital should make sure that a psychiatrist (a doctor who knows about mental disorder) examines you as soon as possible.

↓

The hospital should also give you information about your stay in hospital and your rights. They should help you to get an independent advocate (someone who helps you say what you think about your treatment).

↓

Your doctor should examine you and decide what to do.

↓

If the doctor decides you need treatment and **you agree** you can stay in hospital as a voluntary patient

or

you may leave the hospital and have treatment at home.

↓

If the doctor decides you need treatment and **you do not agree**

↓

your doctor may ask for a short-term detention certificate or a compulsory treatment order.

After 3 days the doctor decides Morag needs treatment. Morag does not agree to this. The doctor gives Morag a short-term detention certificate. Morag has to stay in hospital for treatment for ⏲28 days.

Compulsory treatment order: means you have treatment even if you do not want it.

Short-term detention certificate: this means you can be kept in hospital and given compulsory treatment for up to ⏲28 days.

What is a short-term detention certificate?

The doctor uses this if he/she believes:

- you have a mental disorder

- you cannot decide about your own treatment

- you should be kept in hospital for treatment

- you or someone else is not safe because of your illness.

Your doctor must get your mental health officer to agree. Your mental health officer should speak to you.

↓

Your doctor should talk to your named person. This is someone you choose to look out for you if you have to have treatment. They help decide about your care and treatment.

↓

If you are not in hospital you should be taken to hospital within ⏱3 days. This should be done with care for you. You can be kept in hospital for ⏱28 days.

↓

The hospital should make sure that a psychiatrist (a doctor who knows about mental disorder) examines you as soon as possible.

↓

The hospital should also give you information about your stay in hospital and your rights. They should help you to get the support of an independent advocate (someone who helps you say what you think about your treatment).

↓

Your doctor should:
    examine you
    talk to you to find out your wishes
    read your advance statement if you have one
    decide if you need treatment.

↓

If you need treatment your doctor can give you treatment even if you do not agree.

How long will this last?

This can be for ⏱28 days. The doctor should keep checking how you are.

If you doctor thinks you do not need to be held in hospital:

■ he/she stops the short-term detention certificate

■ you are free to leave the hospital,

or

■ you may stay as a voluntary patient, if you have agreed to do so.

What happens after 28 days?

If your doctor thinks you need more treatment after the ⏱28 days he/she may ask for a compulsory treatment order. This means you have treatment even if you do not want it. You may need to stay in hospital ⏱3-5 more days if your doctors are preparing a compulsory treatment order.

How do I appeal?

You or your named person can ask the Mental Health Tribunal to stop the certificate. The Tribunal is the organisation that decides about the compulsory treatment of people with mental disorder.You can ask a solicitor for advice and to speak for you at the Tribunal. You may be able to get legal aid to pay the solicitor. The solicitor can help you to get this.

13 People involved in criminal proceedings

■ How might the new law affect me?

■ What are the different court orders?

■ Who can help if I am involved with the police or courts?

■ When can the courts use the new law to give me treatment?

■ What are the different orders the courts use?

How might the new law affect me?

If the police believe you have done something wrong you may have to go to court. There may be criminal proceedings. These are the steps the police and courts take to decide if you are guilty or not guilty.

The court can ask a doctor to examine you to find out about your mental disorder.

The doctor gives the court a report.

The report helps the court decide if you need treatment. It also helps the court decide what to do about your case.

The police and courts can use compulsory powers to give you treatment. Compulsory means you have treatment even if you do not want it. They do this when they believe:

■ you have a mental disorder

■ treatment may help you

■ you may not be safe if you do not have treatment

■ there is no other way to give you treatment.

The court use **orders** to say how you should have treatment. These are listed on page 106.

On the next page there is a list of orders with page numbers to help you find the one you need to read about.

Sometimes the police use special powers to help you when you are ill. You have not done anything wrong. They use these powers to help you get care and treatment. You can read more about these emergency powers.

What are the different orders?

1.	Assessment Order	page 109
2.	Treatment Order	page 110
3.	Temporary Compulsion Order	page 111
4.	Acquitted but detained	page 112
5.	Remand on bail for enquiry	page 113
6.	Committal to hospital for enquiry	page 114
7.	Interim Compulsion Order	page 115
8.	Compulsion Order	page 116
9.	Restriction Order	page 118
10.	Hospital Direction	page 119
11.	Transfer for Treatment Direction	page 121
12.	Probation Order with Requirement of Treatment	page 123

Remember, you should ask if you are not sure what order you have been given.

Who can help you if you have to go to court?

Solicitor

You can ask a solicitor to give you advice. You may be able to get legal aid. Legal aid means that you can get help to pay for a solicitor if you cannot afford it. A solicitor should tell you how to get this.

Mental health officer

This is a specially trained social worker who helps people who have a mental disorder. He/she should tell you about your rights and make sure you get the care you need.

Named Person

This is someone you choose to look out for you if you are ill. They help decide about your care and treatment. If you do not choose anyone, your primary carer or nearest relative becomes your named person.

Independent Advocate

Someone who helps you say **what you think** about your care and treatment. They help you get all the information you need and support you at important meetings. They are called "independent" because they are not tied to other services. Your doctor, hospital or social work department should help you find an independent advocate.

Mental Health Tribunal

This is the organisation that decides about your care and treatment if you have compulsory treatment. (This means you have treatment even if you do not want it.)

Mental Welfare Commission

They look after people who need help because of a mental disorder. They make sure all treatment follows the law. You can speak to them at any time if you are unhappy about your care and treatment.

Advance Statements

An advance statement is when you write down how you would like to be treated if you become ill in the future. People caring for you read your advance statement and think about your wishes.

1. Assessment Order

When?

You are waiting for your trial and the court thinks you are ill. They ask a doctor to examine you. The doctor says that you need to go to hospital to be examined.

How long?

The court can order you to stay in hospital for ○28 days. This allows a psychiatrist (specially trained doctor) to examine you. Seven days can be added if the doctor needs more time.

What happens next?

He/she gives a report to the court. The court then decides if you are well enough to go to trial. They can also decide you need to stay in hospital for treatment.

Agree to treatment?

If you do not agree to treatment the doctor must get a second doctor to agree. Then you can be given treatment.

Appeal?

You cannot appeal against this order. Your doctor tells the court if the order should be changed or stopped. Appeal means you ask the court to change its decision.

2. Treatment Order

When?

You are waiting for your trial and the court thinks you are ill. The court can order you to stay in hospital for treatment. The court can only do this if two doctors examine you and agree. One of the doctors must be a psychiatrist.

How long?

There is no fixed time for this order. It can last until the court decides what to do about your case.

Agree to treatment?

If you do not agree to treatment your doctor must get a second doctor to agree. Then you can be given treatment. (The second doctor is chosen by the Mental Welfare Commission.)

Appeal?

You cannot appeal against this order. Your doctor tells the court if the order should be changed or stopped. Appeal means you ask the court to change its decision.

Mental Welfare Commission: they look after those who need help because of a mental disorder. They make sure all treatment follows the law.

3. Temporary Compulsion Order

When?

The court decides that your trial cannot start (or must stop) because of your mental disorder. The court orders you to stay in hospital for treatment. The court can only do this if two doctors examine you and agree.

How long?

There is no fixed time for this order. It lasts until the court decides what to do about your case.

What happens next?

Once the order is made you have to stay in hospital.

The court continues to "examine the facts". This means they try to find out if you did the thing you have been charged with.

Appeal?

You cannot appeal against this order. Appeal means you ask the court to change its decision.

4. Acquitted but detained

When?

At the end of your trial you are acquitted if the court believe **you did not do** the thing you were charged with. (Acquitted means you are cleared of the charge.)

How long?

The court keeps you for ⏱6 hours for a doctor to examine you. The doctor decides what care and treatment you need.

Agree to treatment?

If you do not agree to treatment during these ⏱6 hours you cannot be given treatment.

At the end of your trial you can be acquitted if:

■ the court believe **you did do** the thing you were charged with

but

■ believe you did this because of your mental disorder.

The court can then use other orders to keep you in hospital to be examined or for treatment.

5. Remand on bail for enquiry

When?

At the end of your trial you are found guilty if the court believe you did do the thing you are charged with. If the punishment is prison the court can ask for more information about your mental disorder.

How long?

They give you bail for ⏲3 weeks to go to hospital to be examined.

What happens next?

Bail means you do not have to be in prison. But you may have to follow some conditions (rules). A condition may be that you stay in hospital for doctors to see you. If you do not follow the conditions you have to return to court.

Agree to treatment?

If you do not agree to treatment during this time you cannot be given treatment.

Appeal?

You can appeal if the court does not give you bail. You can appeal against the conditions the court gives you. Appeal means you ask the court to change its decision.

6. Committal to hospital for enquiry

When?

If you are convicted and the punishment is prison, the court may want more information about your health:

- the court asks a doctor to examine you

- the doctor suggests you need to go to hospital for examination.

How long?

The court sends you to hospital for ⏱3 weeks. Another ⏱3 weeks can be added.

What happens next?

In hospital you are examined by doctors. The doctor's report helps the court to decide what to do. You must stay in hospital under this order. If you leave you can be taken back to court.

Agree to treatment?

If you do not agree to treatment and the doctor thinks it is best for you he/she must get a second doctor to agree. Then you can be given treatment.

Appeal?

You can appeal against this order. Appeal means you ask the court to change its decision.

7. Interim Compulsion Order

When?

If you are convicted and the punishment is prison:

- the court asks for more information about your health

- the court asks two doctors to examine you

- the doctors must say you need to go to hospital for examination.

How long?

The court can keep you in hospital for ⏱12 weeks. This order can be renewed every ⏱12 weeks for ⏱1 year.

What happens next?

In hospital doctors examine you and think about what treatment you need. The doctor's report helps the court to decide what to do.

Agree to treatment?

If you do not agree to treatment your doctor must get a second doctor to agree. Then you can be given treatment. (The second doctor is chosen by the Mental Welfare Commission.)

Appeal?

You can appeal to the court against the order being made. Appeal means you ask the court to change its decision. You cannot appeal against it being renewed. Your doctor tells the court if the order needs to be changed or stopped.

8. Compulsion Order

When?

If you are convicted and the punishment is prison the court can decide not to send you to prison. They can decide:

- you must stay in hospital for treatment

or

- you must have treatment in the community.

You are examined by two doctors (one must be a psychiatrist). They must believe:

- you have a mental disorder

- you need treatment to keep you safe

- you need treatment to keep others safe.

How long?

This order is for ⏱6 months. Your psychiatrist must keep checking your health. He/she can ask the Tribunal to change the order or stop it.

After ⏱6 months your psychiatrist can renew it for another ⏱6 months. After that it can be renewed for ⏱12 months at a time.

Treatment in the Community

The court tells you:

■ where you must go to get care and treatment

■ where you must live. Your mental health officer must agree if you wish to move somewhere else

■ the people who must visit you:

  ■ your mental health officer

  ■ your doctor

  ■ any person your doctor says should give you care or treatment.

If you do not follow the order your case may go to the Tribunal to decide. You can be taken to hospital for your own safety.

Agree to treatment?

If you do not agree to treatment your doctor must get a second doctor to agree. Then you can be given treatment. The second doctor is chosen by the Mental Welfare Commission. This is the organisation that looks after those who need help because of a mental disorder.

Appeal?

■ You can appeal to the court against the order being made. Appeal means you ask the court to change its decision.

■ You and your named person can ask the Tribunal to change or stop the order. The Tribunal then decides.

■ The Mental Welfare Commission can also stop the order or ask the Tribunal to decide.

9. Restriction Order

When?

If you have a Compulsion Order (see pages 116 and 117) the court can also give you a Restriction Order.

This means that Scottish Ministers must agree for:

■ you to move to another hospital

■ to leave the hospital.

How long?

There is no fixed time for the Compulsion Order. It goes on until the Restriction Order is stopped.

Your psychiatrist and Scottish Ministers must review the order. If they want to change it they must ask the Tribunal.

The Tribunal reviews your case every ⏱2 years.

Appeal?

You can appeal against this order. Appeal means you ask the court to change its decision.

■ You and your named person can ask the Tribunal to make changes.

■ The Tribunal can change or stop the order.

■ The Mental Welfare Commission can ask the Tribunal to decide.

Mental Welfare Commission: the organisation that looks after those who need help because of a mental disorder. They make sure all treatment follows the law. You can speak to them at any time if you are unhappy about your care and treatment.

10. Hospital Direction

When?

If you are given a prison sentence the court can decide you need treatment for your mental disorder. You should be examined by two doctors (one should be a psychiatrist). They must believe:

- you have a mental disorder

- you need treatment to keep you and others safe.

How long?

This order ends at the same time as your prison sentence.

If the order stops before your sentence, you go to prison for the rest of the time left.

If you are in hospital at the end of your prison sentence your doctor may think you need to stay in hospital. He/she can ask the Tribunal to decide this.

What happens next?

The Scottish Ministers:

- must agree if you move to another hospital

- must agree if you leave the hospital

- must keep reviewing if you need to be on the order

- can sometimes order you to go to prison for the rest of the sentence.

Agree to treatment?

If you do not agree to treatment your doctor must get a second doctor to agree. Then you can be given treatment. (The second doctor is chosen by the Mental Welfare Commission.)

Appeal?

You can appeal to the court before the order is made. Appeal means you ask the court to change the decision.

The Scottish Ministers can also stop the order.

You and your named person can ask the Tribunal to decide.

The Mental Welfare Commission can ask the Tribunal to decide.

Mental Welfare Commission: the organisation that looks after those who need help because of a mental disorder. They make sure all treatment follows the law. You can speak to them at any time if you are unhappy about your care and treatment.

11. Transfer for Treatment Direction

When?

If you are in prison and your doctors believe:

■ you have a mental disorder

■ you need treatment to keep you and others safe

you can be taken to hospital for care and treatment.

What happens?

The Scottish Ministers:

■ must agree if you move to another hospital

■ must agree if you leave the hospital

■ must keep reviewing if you need to be on the order

■ can sometimes order you to go to prison for the rest of the sentence.

How long?

This order ends at the same time as your sentence.

If the order stops before your prison sentence you go to prison for the rest of the time left.

If you are in hospital at the end of your prison sentence your doctor may think you need to stay in hospital. He/she can ask the Tribunal to decide this.

Agree to treatment?

If you do not agree to treatment your doctor must get a second doctor to agree. Then you will be given treatment. (The second doctor will be chosen by the Mental Welfare Commission).

Appeal?

■   You can appeal to the court against the order being made. Appeal means you ask the court to change the decision.

■ You and your named person can ask the Tribunal to stop it.

■ The Tribunal can decide to stop the order.

■ The Scottish Ministers can also stop the order.

■ The Mental Welfare Commission can ask the Tribunal to decide.

Mental Welfare Commission: the organisation that looks after those who need help because of a mental disorder. They make sure all treatment follows the law. You can speak to them at any time if you are unhappy about your care and treatment.

12. Probation Order with Requirement of Treatment

When?

If you leave prison on probation you have to follow certain rules. This order says you must have treatment for your mental disorder.

It can ask you to go to a surgery or a hospital for treatment. The court cannot give you this order unless you agree.

The order must be recommended by:

- a psychiatrist

- the doctor who will be giving you the treatment

- your supervising officer (someone your local authority appoints to look after you on probation).

How Long?

The order can last for up to ⏱3 years.

What happens if you do not keep to the rules?

You may have to go back to court:

- if you do not keep your appointments

- if you refuse treatment

- if you leave hospital without permission.

Agree to treatment?

If you do not agree to treatment during this time you cannot be given treatment.

14 How do I appeal?

- What is an appeal?
- How do I appeal?
- When can I appeal to the Tribunal?
- When can I not appeal to the Tribunal?
- When can I appeal to the court?
- What is the Mental Welfare Commission?

What is an appeal?

If you become ill, you may have compulsory care or treatment. This means you can be given treatment even if you do not want it. The Mental Health Tribunal is the organisation that decides if you need compulsory care and treatment.

If you do not agree, you can appeal. This means you can:

■ tell the Tribunal you do not agree

■ ask the Tribunal to change their decision.

Darren has a compulsory treatment order. He thinks he is now much better. He appeals to the Tribunal to stop his order. His named person, Sean, helps him to do this.

How do I appeal?

You or your named person or your solicitor should write to the Tribunal. Your named person is someone you choose to look out for you if you have to have treatment. They help decide about your care and treatment.

Darren writes to the Tribunal office. He tells the Tribunal why they should stop the order. Sean helps him with the letter.

You must tell them:

1. Your name and address.

2. Your named person's name and address.

3. Your address if you are in hospital or living at another place.

4. The reasons for your appeal.

What happens next?

The Tribunal arranges a hearing. This is a special meeting.

Darren and Sean, his named person, go to the Tribunal hearing. Darren's doctor and mental health officer also go to the meeting.

The Tribunal read and discuss all the information about you and your case. They listen to what everyone has to say. They then decide what to do about your care and treatment.,

The Tribunal read all the information. This includes reports from Darren's doctor and his mental health officer. They listen to Darren and everyone else. They decide to stop Darren's compulsory treatment order.

If your appeal is successful, the Tribunal changes the decision about your care and treatment.

If your appeal is not successful, the Tribunal tell you how to make another appeal. You may be able to appeal to the Tribunal again or you may be able to appeal to the court.

Mental health officer: is a specially trained social worker who helps people who have a mental disorder. He/she should tell you about your rights and make sure you get the care you need.

When can I appeal to the Tribunal?

1. **Short-term detention certificate**

   You can be held in hospital for ①28 days for treatment.

   You and your named person can appeal and have this stopped.

2. **Compulsory treatment order**

   You have treatment even if you do not want it.

   You and your named person can appeal. You can ask the Tribunal to change or cancel your order. (Usually after ①3 months.)

   If you are not successful, you can appeal again.

3. **Compulsion order**

   The court says you must have treatment in hospital or in the community for ①6 months.

   You and your named person can appeal. You can ask the Tribunal to change or stop the order.

4. Restriction order

If you have a Compulsion Order the court can also give you a Restriction Order. This means that Scottish Ministers must agree for you to move to another hospital or to leave the hospital.

You and your named person can appeal to the Tribunal:

- to make changes to the order

- to cancel/stop the order.

5. Hospital Direction/Transfer for Treatment Direction

If you are given a prison sentence, the court can give you a Hospital Direction. This means you must have hospital treatment for your mental disorder.

The court can also give you a Transfer for Treatment Direction. This means Scottish Ministers must agree for you to leave hospital or move hospital.

You and your named person can appeal to the Tribunal:

- to make changes to this order

- to cancel/stop this order.

If you are successful, you return to prison for the rest of your prison sentence.

6. Security levels

If you are in the State Hospital, you can appeal to the Tribunal. You can say that you do not need to be held with so much security. Others can also appeal for you. These are:

- your named person

- your guardian or welfare attorney

- Mental Welfare Commission the organisation that looks after those who need help because of a mental disorder.

If you are successful, you will be moved to another hospital in the time agreed by the Tribunal. If you are not the hospital must tell the Tribunal and there will be another hearing.

7. Transfer to a hospital in Scotland

Your doctor may think you should be moved to another hospital for care and treatment. If you do not agree, you or your named person can appeal to the Tribunal.

If you are successful, you will not have to move hospital. If you have already moved then you can go back to the hospital you were in.

You must appeal within ⏱28 days of being told. (If you are moving to the State Hospital you must appeal within ⏱12 weeks.)

8. Transfer to a hospital outside Scotland

Your doctor may think you should be moved to a hospital in another country. If you do not agree you should tell Scottish Ministers within ⏲7 days.

You can appeal to the Tribunal. You cannot be moved until the Tribunal has decided your appeal.

You cannot appeal to the Tribunal in Scotland <u>after</u> you have moved. (You can appeal to the court in the country you have been moved to)

9. Appeal against unlawful detention

If you are in hospital and not having compulsory treatment, you can discharge yourself. This means you can leave when you want to.

If the hospital does not allow you to leave, you can appeal to the Tribunal. You can ask the Tribunal to tell the hospital to discharge you. Others can appeal for you:

- your named person

- your mental health officer

- the Mental Welfare Commission

- your guardian or welfare attorney

- others who look after your care and welfare – your family

- if you are a child your parent/carer.

When can I not appeal to the Tribunal?

1. Emergency detention order

Emergency detention order means you can be kept in hospital and have treatment for ☉3 days.

You cannot appeal.

2. An interim compulsory treatment order

You cannot appeal.

The Tribunal must hold a hearing to agree to the interim order within ☉28 days of making the order. You will be able to say what you think at the hearing.

3. An interim compulsion order

You cannot appeal.

The Tribunal must hold a hearing to agree to the interim order within ☉28 days of making the order. You will be able to say what you think at the hearing.

4. Transfer for treatment

If you are on remand, and sent to hospital for assessment or treatment (or convicted but awaiting final disposal of your case) you cannot appeal to the Tribunal as the court is still considering your case.

When can I appeal to the court?

When the Tribunal decides about your appeal, they tell you what to do if you are unhappy about it.

You can appeal to the court within ⏱21 days.

If your appeal is successful, the court:

■ gives you a new decision

or

■ sends the case back to the Tribunal.

What is the Mental Welfare Commission?

The Mental Welfare Commission is the organisation who looks after people who need help because of a mental disorder. They make sure all treatment follows the law. If you or your carer want to ask about your rights you can phone ☎ 0800 389 6809 (open 9 - 5 from Monday - Friday).

If the Commission is unhappy about your care and treatment, they find out more about your needs.

The new law gives the Commission power to change compulsory orders. They only do this in very special situations.

They usually ask ask the Tribunal to decide what is best for you.

Advance statement: when you write down how you would like to be treated if you become ill in the future.

Appeal: means you ask the court or the tribunal to change their decision.

Compulsory treatment order: means you have treatment even if you do not want it

Emergency detention certificate: you can be kept in hospital and given treatment for no more than ☉3 days.

Guardian: someone appointed by the court to make decisions for you if you are unable to decide for yourself.

Legal aid: means that you can get help to pay for a solicitor if you cannot afford it. A solicitor should tell you how to apply for legal aid.

Independent advocate: someone who helps you say what you think about your treatment. They are called 'independent' because they are not tied to other services. Your doctor, hospital or social work department should help you find an independent advocate.

Mental disorder: is the word used in the law to describe someone who has:

- a mental illness
- a learning disability
- a personality disorder.

Mental health officer: a specially trained social worker who helps people who have a mental disorder. He/she should tell you about your rights and make sure you get the care you need.

Mental Health Tribunal: the organisation that decides about the compulsory treatment of people with mental disorder.

Mental Welfare Commission: the organisation that looks after those who need help because of a mental disorder. They make sure all treatment follows the law. You can speak to them at any time if you are unhappy about your care and treatment.

Named person: someone you choose to look out for you if you have to have treatment. They help to make decisions about your care and treatment.

Primary carer: the carer who gives you all or most of the care and support.

Short-term detention certificate: this means you can be kept in hospital and given compulsory treatment for up to ⏱28 days.

Voluntary patient: this is someone who agrees to have treatment for their mental disorder.

Welfare attorney: someone you choose to decide about your care and treatment if you become ill and cannot decide for yourself.

Witness: someone who checks and signs your advance statement.

16 Where else can I get help or advice?

Bipolar Fellowship Scotland

Studio 1016
Abbeymill Business Centre
Seedhill Road
PAISLEY PA1 1TJ
telephone: 0141 560 2050
website: www.bipolarscotland.org.uk

Depression Alliance Scotland

3 Grosvenor Gardens
EDINBURGH EH12 5JU
telephone: 0131 467 7701
website: www.depressionalliance.org

Enable

6th Floor
7 Buchanan Street
GLASGOW G1 3HL
telephone: 0141 226 4541
website: www.enable.org.uk

Mental Health Tribunal for Scotland

1st Floor, Bothwell House
Hamilton Business Park
Caird Park
HAMILTON ML3 0QA
telephone: 01698 390 000
website: www.mhtscot.org

✉ Mental Welfare Commission for Scotland

Floor K, Argyle House
3 Lady Lawson Street
EDINBURGH EH3 9SH
telephone: 0131 222 6111
☎ service user and carer freephone: 0800 389 6809
💻 website: www.mwcscot.org.uk

✉ National Schizophrenia Fellowship (Scotland)

Claremont House
130 East Claremont Street
EDINBURGH EH7 4LB
☎ telephone: 0131 557 8969
💻 website: www.nsfscot.org.uk

✉ People First (Scotland)

77 – 79 Easter Road
EDINBURGH EH7 5PW
☎ telephone: 0131 478 7707

✉ Scottish Association for Mental Health (SAMH)

Cumbrae House
15 Carlton Court
GLASGOW G5 9JP
☎ telephone: 0141 568 7000
💻 website: www.samh.org.uk

▣ Scottish Commission for the Regulation of Care

11 Riverside Drive
DUNDEE DD1 4NY
📞 telephone: 0845 60 30 890
💻 website: www.carecommission.com

▣ Scottish Consortium for Learning Disability (SCLD)

The Adelphi Centre
Room 16
12 Commercial Road
GLASGOW G5 0PQ
📞 telephone: 0141 418 5420
💻 website: www.scld.org.uk

▣ Scottish Independent Advocacy Alliance

Melrose House
69A George Street
EDINBURGH EH2 2JG
📞 telephone: 0131 260 5381
💻 website: www.siaa.org.uk

▣ The Office of the Public Guardian

Hadrian House
Callendar Business Park
Callendar Road
FALKIRK FK1 1XR
📞 telephone: 01324 678 300
💻 website: www.publicguardian-scotland.gov.uk